IXL MATH WORKBOOK

GRADE 1
ADDITION

ISBN: 9781947569461
24 23 22 21 20 1 2 3 4 5

Printed in the USA

Fill in the blanks.

2 leaves and 2 leaves is ___4___ leaves.

4 cupcakes and 3 cupcakes is _____ cupcakes.

1 duck and 4 ducks is _____ ducks.

Fill in the blanks.

1 puzzle piece and 8 puzzle pieces is _____ puzzle pieces.

3 butterflies and 2 butterflies is _____ butterflies.

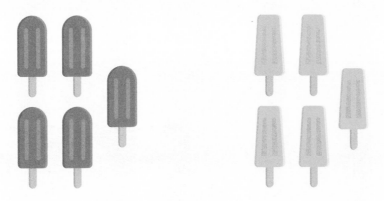

5 ice pops and 5 ice pops is _____ ice pops.

For more practice, visit IXL.com or the IXL mobile app and enter this code in the search bar.

IXL.com
skill ID
E8D

Fill in the blanks.

___4___ horses and ___6___ horses is ___10___ horses.

_____ hamsters and _____ hamsters is _____ hamsters.

_____ cows and _____ cows is _____ cows.

You can also use the words **plus** and **equals** to show addition. Fill in the blanks.

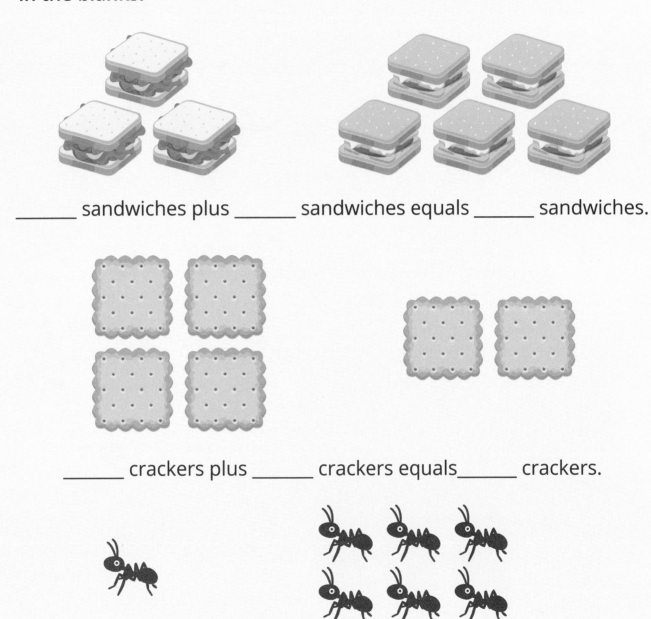

_____ sandwiches plus _____ sandwiches equals _____ sandwiches.

_____ crackers plus _____ crackers equals_____ crackers.

_____ ant plus _____ ants equals _____ ants.

Draw a picture to solve.

Logan found 2 coins. Leo found 3 coins. How many coins did they find?

_____2____ coins plus _____3____ coins equals _____5____ coins.

Joy saw 1 bird's nest. Mike saw 3 bird's nests. How many nests did they see?

_____ nest plus _____ nests equals _____ nests.

Dan made 4 snowballs. Kira made 2 snowballs. How many snowballs did they make in all?

_____ snowballs plus _____ snowballs equals _____ snowballs.

Draw a picture to solve.

Liam baked 4 pies. Ally baked 5 pies. How many pies did they bake?

_____ pies plus _____ pies equals _____ pies.

Gia has 3 books. Kelsey also has 3 books. How many books do they have?

_____ books plus _____ books equals _____ books.

Mandy has 3 hats. Her brother has 4 hats. How many hats do they have?

_____ hats plus _____ hats equals _____ hats.

IXL.com
skill ID
KUH

Let's Learn!

You can use + and = to write an **addition sentence**. The answer is called the **sum**. Here, the **sum** is 6.

4   plus   2   equals   6
4   +   2   =   6

Fill in the circles with + or = to write the addition sentence.

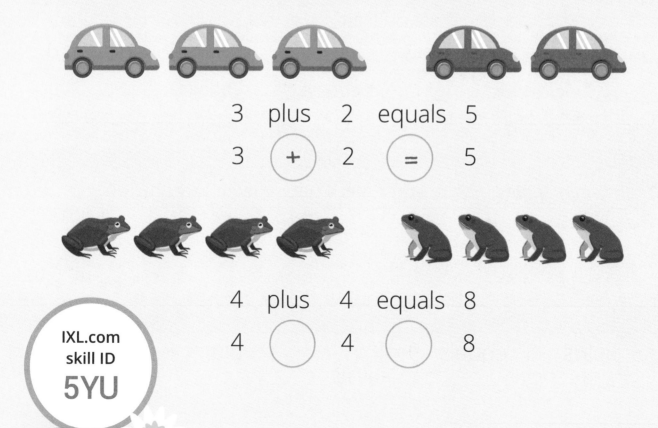

3   plus   2   equals   5
3   (+)   2   (=)   5

4   plus   4   equals   8
4   ( )   4   ( )   8

IXL.com
skill ID
5YU

Keep going! Fill in the circles with + or = to write the addition sentence.

1   plus   5   equals   6

1   ◯   5   ◯   6

Write the addition sentence.

5   plus   2   equals   7

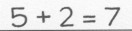

5 + 2 = 7

2   plus   2   equals   4

_____

3   plus   6   equals   9

_____

1   plus   8   equals   9

_____

Write the addition sentence for each animal.

 $\underline{\hspace{1cm} 2 + 2 = 4 \hspace{1cm}}$

 $\underline{\hspace{4cm}}$

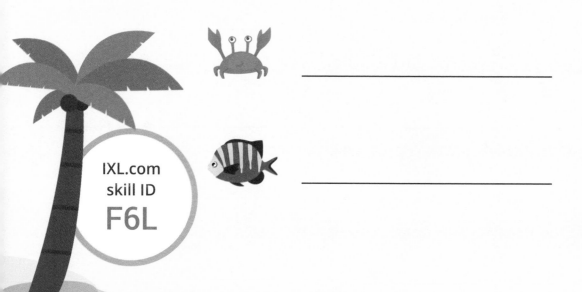

Write the addition sentence.

There are 4 children at the park. Another 4 children join them. How many children are at the park?

___4___ + ___4___ = ___8___ children

Pedro walked 3 dogs last week. He walked 3 more dogs this week. How many dogs did he walk in all?

_____ + _____ = _____ dogs

Gina saw 8 birds and 2 frogs on her walk. How many animals did she see?

_____ + _____ = _____ animals

Molly and Tia are eating lunch. Then 3 friends come over to eat with them. How many friends are eating lunch?

_____ + _____ = _____ friends

IXL.com
skill ID

P6D

A number line shows numbers in order. The numbers get bigger as you count on.

Circle the number that is 3 more than 1.

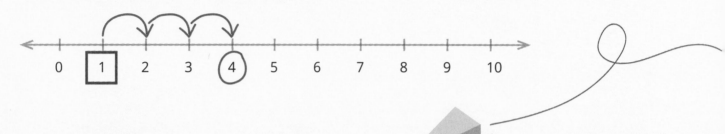

Circle the number that is 2 more than 6.

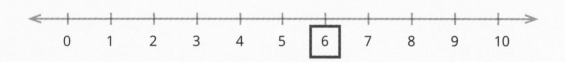

Circle the number that is 1 more than 9.

Circle the number that is 4 more than 4.

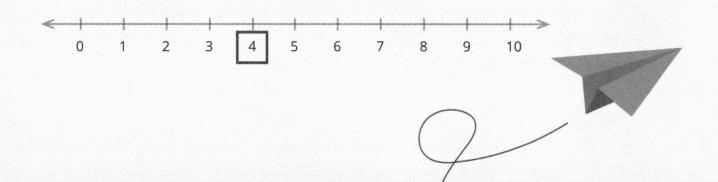

You can add with a number line! Count on to add.

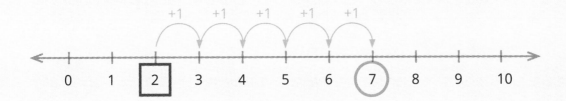

$$\underline{\quad 2 \quad} + \underline{\quad 5 \quad} = \underline{\quad 7 \quad}$$

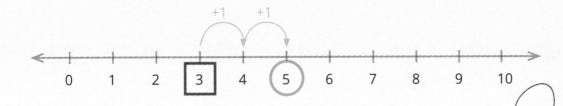

$$\underline{\qquad} + \underline{\qquad} = \underline{\qquad}$$

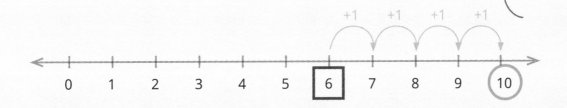

$$\underline{\qquad} + \underline{\qquad} = \underline{\qquad}$$

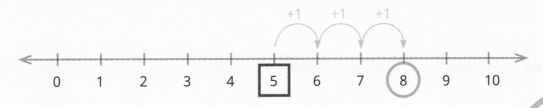

$$\underline{\qquad} + \underline{\qquad} = \underline{\qquad}$$

Use the number line to add.

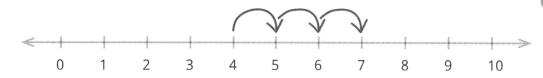

4 + 3 = ___7___

1 + 4 = _____

4 + 5 = _____

2 + 6 = _____

Show some ways to make 4 and 5. Fill in the blanks.

$\underline{\quad 3 \quad} + \underline{\quad 1 \quad} = \underline{\quad 4 \quad}$

$\underline{\quad\quad} + \underline{\quad\quad} = \underline{\quad\quad}$

$\underline{\quad\quad} + \underline{\quad\quad} = \underline{\quad\quad}$

$\underline{\quad\quad} + \underline{\quad\quad} = \underline{\quad\quad}$

$\underline{\quad\quad} + \underline{\quad\quad} = \underline{\quad\quad}$

$\underline{\quad\quad} + \underline{\quad\quad} = \underline{\quad\quad}$

$\underline{\quad\quad} + \underline{\quad\quad} = \underline{\quad\quad}$

Add.

$1 + 3 = \underline{4}$ $\qquad\qquad$ $2 + 2 = \underline{}$

$2 + 3 = \underline{}$ $\qquad\qquad$ $3 + 1 = \underline{}$

$1 + 4 = \underline{}$ $\qquad\qquad$ $3 + 2 = \underline{}$

Write the missing number.

$2 + \underline{3} = 5$ $\qquad\qquad$ $\underline{} + 1 = 4$

$\underline{} + 1 = 5$ $\qquad\qquad$ $2 + \underline{} = 4$

$\underline{} + 3 = 4$ $\qquad\qquad$ $3 + \underline{} = 5$

IXL.com
skill ID
JRS

When you add 0 to a number, the number stays the same!

$$3 + 0 = 3$$

Add.

$4 + 0 =$ _____

$0 + 3 =$ _____

$0 + 5 =$ _____

$2 + 0 =$ _____

$0 + 4 =$ _____

IXL.com
skill ID
UFN

Add.

3 + 1 = _____   1 + 0 = _____

2 + 2 = _____   1 + 1 = _____

5 + 0 = _____   3 + 2 = _____

1 + 2 = _____   4 + 1 = _____

1 + 3 = _____   0 + 2 = _____

Show some ways to make 6 and 7. Fill in the blanks.

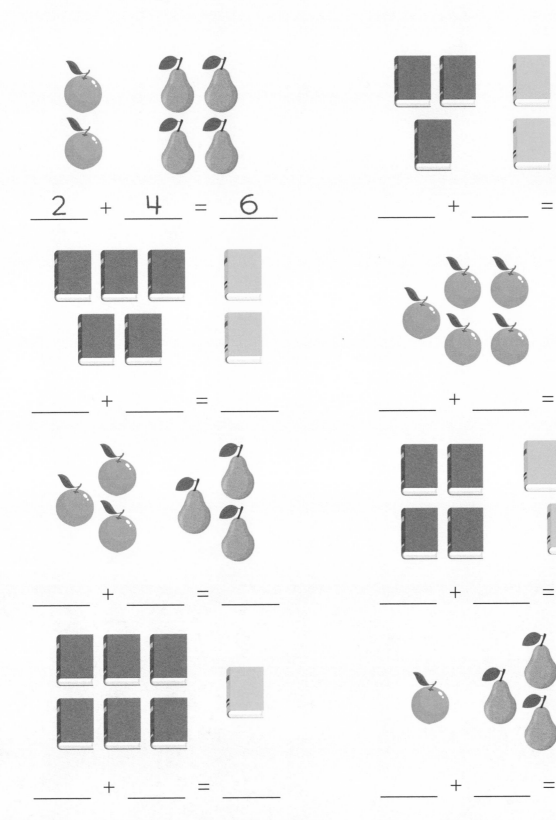

_2_ + _4_ = _6_

____ + ____ = ____

____ + ____ = ____

____ + ____ = ____

____ + ____ = ____

____ + ____ = ____

____ + ____ = ____

____ + ____ = ____

Add.

$1 + 5 = \underline{6}$

$3 + 4 = \underline{}$

$3 + 2 = \underline{}$

$2 + 1 = \underline{}$

$5 + 2 = \underline{}$

$3 + 3 = \underline{}$

$1 + 6 = \underline{}$

$3 + 0 = \underline{}$

$4 + 1 = \underline{}$

$2 + 4 = \underline{}$

Show some ways to make 8 and 9. Fill in the blanks.

$\underline{\quad4\quad} + \underline{\quad5\quad} = \underline{\quad9\quad}$ \qquad $\underline{\qquad} + \underline{\qquad} = \underline{\qquad}$

$\underline{\qquad} + \underline{\qquad} = \underline{\qquad}$ \qquad $\underline{\qquad} + \underline{\qquad} = \underline{\qquad}$

$\underline{\qquad} + \underline{\qquad} = \underline{\qquad}$ \qquad $\underline{\qquad} + \underline{\qquad} = \underline{\qquad}$

$\underline{\qquad} + \underline{\qquad} = \underline{\qquad}$ \qquad $\underline{\qquad} + \underline{\qquad} = \underline{\qquad}$

Add.

$2 + 7 =$ _____

$3 + 5 =$ _____

$6 + 1 =$ _____

$4 + 2 =$ _____

$6 + 2 =$ _____

$3 + 6 =$ _____

$1 + 7 =$ _____

$1 + 3 =$ _____

$2 + 2 =$ _____

$0 + 4 =$ _____

$2 + 5 =$ _____

$4 + 4 =$ _____

$4 + 1 =$ _____

$5 + 4 =$ _____

Add.

$1 + 5 =$ _____

$0 + 7 =$ _____

$2 + 3 =$ _____

$6 + 3 =$ _____

$1 + 2 =$ _____

$3 + 3 =$ _____

$2 + 6 =$ _____

$1 + 4 =$ _____

$9 + 0 =$ _____

$7 + 1 =$ _____

$3 + 4 =$ _____

$4 + 5 =$ _____

IXL.com
skill ID
VSE

Write the missing number.

$3 + \underline{\ 3\ } = 6$ $2 + \underline{\hspace{1cm}} = 7$

$1 + \underline{\hspace{1cm}} = 5$ $\underline{\hspace{1cm}} + 0 = 8$

$3 + \underline{\hspace{1cm}} = 9$ $\underline{\hspace{1cm}} + 1 = 7$

$\underline{\hspace{1cm}} + 4 = 8$ $\underline{\hspace{1cm}} + 4 = 9$

$2 + \underline{\hspace{1cm}} = 9$ $7 + \underline{\hspace{1cm}} = 8$

Add. Match the addition problem to its sum.

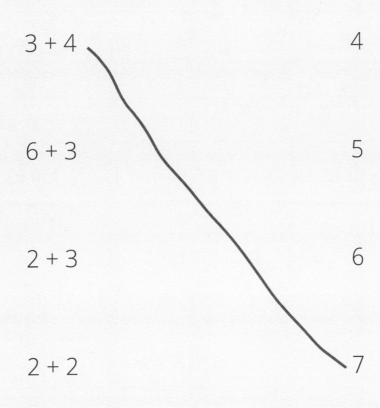

3 + 4   4

6 + 3   5

2 + 3   6

2 + 2   7

7 + 1   8

4 + 2   9

Write the addition sentence.

Zoe picks 3 red flowers. She also picks 4 yellow flowers. How many flowers does she pick?

___3___ + ___4___ = ___7___ flowers

Kayla ate 2 fruit snacks. Then she ate 6 more. How many fruit snacks did Kayla eat?

_____ + _____ = _____ fruit snacks

Andy read 2 books. Later, he read 5 more books. How many books did Andy read?

_____ + _____ = _____ books

There are 4 squirrels in a tree. There are 5 more squirrels in another tree. How many squirrels is that in all?

_____ + _____ = _____ squirrels

Show some ways to make 10. Fill in the blanks.

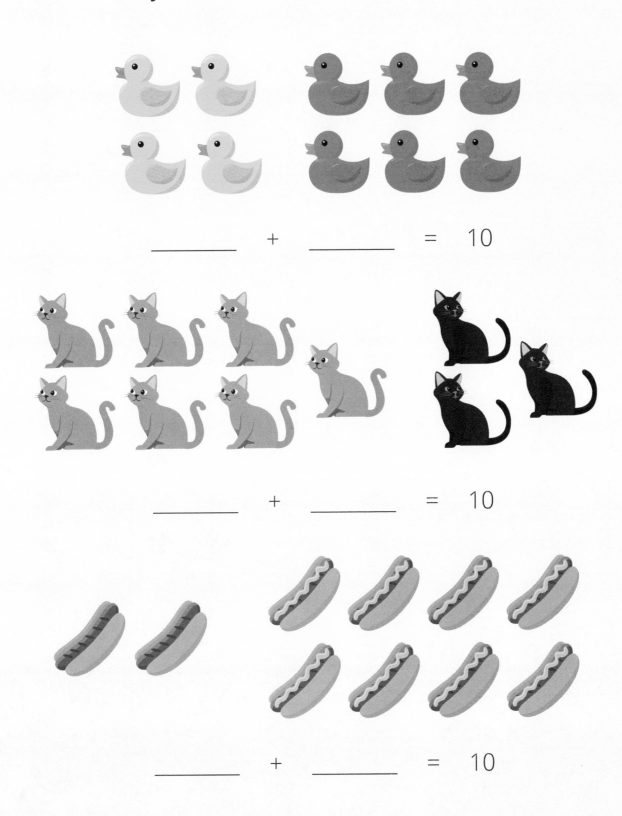

_____ + _____ = 10

_____ + _____ = 10

_____ + _____ = 10

Write the numbers that make 10.

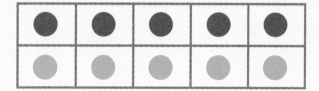

____5____ + ____5____ = 10

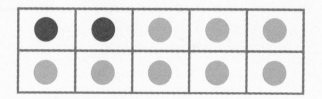

_____ + _____ = 10

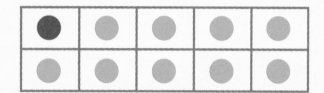

_____ + _____ = 10

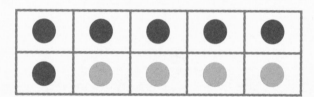

_____ + _____ = 10

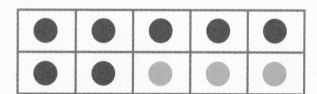

_____ + _____ = 10

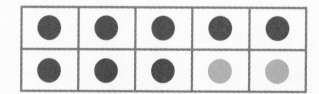

_____ + _____ = 10

Draw dots to make 10. Write the missing number.

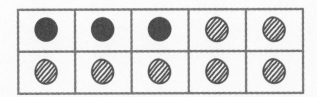

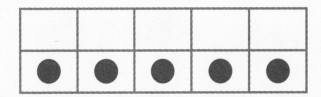

$$3 + \underline{\quad 7 \quad} = 10$$

$$\underline{\qquad} + 5 = 10$$

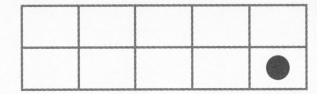

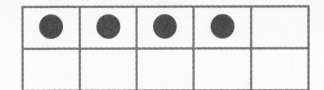

$$\underline{\qquad} + 1 = 10$$

$$4 + \underline{\qquad} = 10$$

Keep going! Grab two colors. Draw dots and write numbers to make 10.

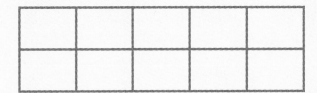

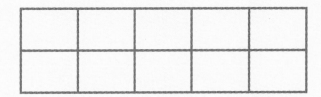

$$\underline{\qquad} + \underline{\qquad} = 10$$

$$\underline{\qquad} + \underline{\qquad} = 10$$

Write the missing number.

6 + ___4___ = 10   _____ + 5 = 10

3 + 7 = _____   8 + _____ = 10

_____ + 1 = 10   4 + _____ = 10

7 + _____ = 10   2 + 8 = _____

_____ + 10 = 10   1 + _____ = 10

Use the numbers to find all the ways to make 10! Cross out each number when you use it.

0	~~1~~	2	3	4	5	6	7	8	9	10
0	1	2	3	4	5	6	7	8	~~9~~	10

___1___ + ___9___ = 10   _____ + _____ = 10

_____ + _____ = 10   _____ + _____ = 10

_____ + _____ = 10   _____ + _____ = 10

_____ + _____ = 10   _____ + _____ = 10

_____ + _____ = 10   _____ + _____ = 10

_____ + _____ = 10

Ana is filling 10 goodie bags for her birthday party. Help her by answering each question!

Ana has 3 blue bouncy balls and 7 purple bouncy balls. How many bouncy balls does she have?

_____ bouncy balls

Ana has 6 green party hats and 4 yellow party hats. How many party hats does she have?

_____ party hats

Ana wants to put a red lollipop in each bag. She has 5 lollipops. How many more lollipops does she need?

_____ lollipops

Add. Find the path from start to finish. Step only on the squares that add to 10.

START ↓

3 + 7	1 + 9	2 + 3
3 + 5	2 + 8	3 + 3
1 + 5	5 + 5	4 + 6
2 + 6	4 + 4	9 + 1
2 + 7	6 + 3	7 + 3

FINISH ↓

Become an IXL member for unlimited math practice. Join today!

Visit www.ixl.com/workbook/1a for details.

Ms. Moore made a picture graph. It shows baby animals at her farm. Look at the picture graph.

Baby animals at Ms. Moore's farm

| Goats | |
| Sheep | |

Use the picture graph to answer each question.

How many baby goats are there?   ___5___ baby goats

How many baby sheep are there?   _____ baby sheep

Are there more baby goats or baby sheep at the farm?   _____

How many baby animals are there in all?   _____ baby animals

Connor and his friends ate snacks at the movies. Look at the picture graph of their snacks.

Snacks at the movies

Popcorn	🍿 🍿 🍿 🍿 🍿
Nachos	🧇 🧇
Hot dogs	🌭 🌭 🌭

Use the picture graph to answer each question.

How many hot dogs did they eat? _____ hot dogs

How many boxes of popcorn did they eat? _____ boxes

Connor's friends bought 2 more trays of nachos. How many trays is that in all?

_____ trays

IXL.com skill ID
GFA

Mary asked her friends if they go to summer camp. She made a bar graph of their answers.

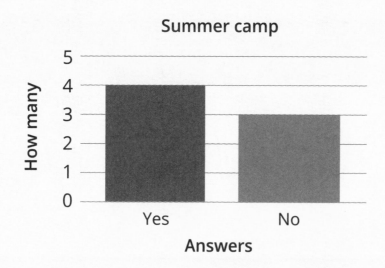

Use the bar graph to answer each question.

How many of Mary's friends go to summer camp?   _____4_____ friends

How many of her friends do not go to summer camp?   _____ friends

How many friends did Mary ask in all?   _____ friends

Jake made a bar graph of the colors his friends like.

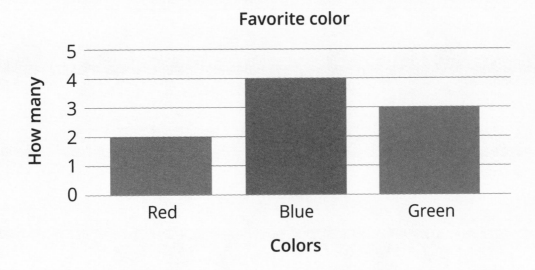

Use the bar graph to answer each question.

What color did most of Jake's friends pick? _____

How many friends picked red? _____ friends

How many friends picked blue or green? _____ friends

How many friends did Jake ask in all? _____ friends

Write the addition sentences for each pair of pictures.

__2__ + __1__ = __3__

_____ + _____ = _____

_____ + _____ = _____

_____ + _____ = _____

_____ + _____ = _____

_____ + _____ = _____

LOOK AGAIN! Look at each pair of pictures. The order is swapped. Has the sum changed?

Keep going! Add.

$3 + 4 = \underline{7}$

$4 + 3 = \underline{7}$

$2 + 7 = \underline{}$

$7 + 2 = \underline{}$

$1 + 5 = \underline{}$

$5 + 1 = \underline{}$

$2 + 8 = \underline{}$

$8 + 2 = \underline{}$

$6 + 2 = \underline{}$

$2 + 6 = \underline{}$

$2 + 5 = \underline{}$

$5 + 2 = \underline{}$

$6 + 3 = \underline{}$

$3 + 6 = \underline{}$

$7 + 3 = \underline{}$

$3 + 7 = \underline{}$

$9 + 1 = \underline{}$

$1 + 9 = \underline{}$

$4 + 5 = \underline{}$

$5 + 4 = \underline{}$

For more practice, visit IXL.com or the IXL mobile app and enter this code in the search bar.

IXL.com skill ID **Y8Y**

Draw the missing objects to make the addition sentence true.
Write the number of objects you draw.

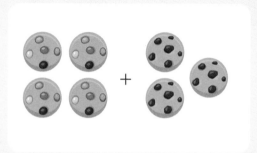 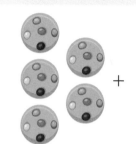 

4   +   3   =   5   +   __2__

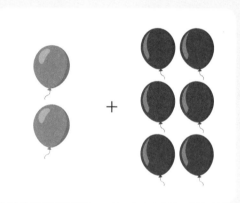 

2   +   6   =   4   +   _____

4   +   6   =   7   +   _____

Write the missing number.

5 + __2__ = 3 + 4

$\underbrace{}$

7

2 + 3 = 1 + _____

_____ + 4 = 2 + 7

2 + 8 = 4 + _____

3 + 3 = 5 + _____

_____ + 5 = 6 + 4

Write numbers to make each addition sentence true.

4 + 4 = __2__ + __6__

_____ + _____ = 7 + 2

_____ + _____ = 3 + 2

2 + 5 = _____ + _____

2 + 4 = _____ + _____

_____ + _____ = 4 + 6

Add. Draw a line between the matching answers.

$3 + 2 = 5$	$1 + 3$
$4 + 4$	$3 + 3$
$5 + 1$	$9 + 1$
$2 + 8$	$2 + 5$
$2 + 2$	$3 + 5$
$3 + 4$	$1 + 4 = 5$

Let's Learn!

You can add across or add down! Both ways give the same answer.

Across

$$3 + 6 = 9$$

Down

$$\begin{array}{r} 3 \\ + 6 \\ \hline 9 \end{array}$$

Add.

6 + 1 = _____

$$\begin{array}{r} 6 \\ + 1 \\ \hline \end{array}$$

2 + 4 = _____

$$\begin{array}{r} 2 \\ + 4 \\ \hline \end{array}$$

5 + 3 = _____

$$\begin{array}{r} 5 \\ + 3 \\ \hline \end{array}$$

Add across. Then write the numbers to add down.

3 + 7 = ___10___

$$\begin{array}{r} 3 \\ + 7 \\ \hline 10 \end{array}$$

3 + 4 = _____

5 + 2 = _____

1 + 8 = _____

Add.

$$\begin{array}{r} 2 \\ +\,5 \\ \hline 7 \end{array}$$

$$\begin{array}{r} 3 \\ +\,2 \\ \hline \end{array}$$

$$\begin{array}{r} 7 \\ +\,2 \\ \hline \end{array}$$

$$\begin{array}{r} 3 \\ +\,3 \\ \hline \end{array}$$

$$\begin{array}{r} 6 \\ +\,2 \\ \hline \end{array}$$

$$\begin{array}{r} 4 \\ +\,6 \\ \hline \end{array}$$

$$\begin{array}{r} 1 \\ +\,3 \\ \hline \end{array}$$

$$\begin{array}{r} 5 \\ +\,1 \\ \hline \end{array}$$

$$\begin{array}{r} 4 \\ +\,4 \\ \hline \end{array}$$

$$\begin{array}{r} 0 \\ +\,7 \\ \hline \end{array}$$

$$\begin{array}{r} 7 \\ +\,3 \\ \hline \end{array}$$

$$\begin{array}{r} 5 \\ +\,4 \\ \hline \end{array}$$

IXL.com
skill ID
WUL

Write each doubles fact.

___3___ + ___3___ = ___6___   _____ + _____ = _____

  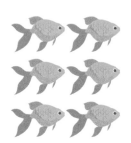 

_____ + _____ = _____   _____ + _____ = _____

_____ + _____ = _____   _____ + _____ = _____

Add across.

$4 + 4 =$ _____ $5 + 5 =$ _____

$6 + 6 =$ _____ $3 + 3 =$ _____

$8 + 8 =$ _____ $9 + 9 =$ _____

Add down.

$$\begin{array}{r} 4 \\ + 4 \\ \hline \end{array}$$ $$\begin{array}{r} 7 \\ + 7 \\ \hline \end{array}$$ $$\begin{array}{r} 8 \\ + 8 \\ \hline \end{array}$$

IXL.com
skill ID
DFT

Use doubles facts to answer each question.

Glen and Cora made cards for their friends. Glen made 4 cards. Cora made 4 cards. How many cards did they make?

_____ cards

Devon saw 6 kites at the park. Mike saw 6 other kites. How many kites did they see in all?

_____ kites

Aaron and Meg each have 5 toy trains. How many trains do they have in all?

_____ trains

An ant has 3 legs on each side of its body. How many legs does an ant have?

_____ legs

Let's Learn!

You can use doubles to help with doubles + 1.

$3 + 3 = 6$

$3 + 4 = 7$

Add.

$4 + 4 = \underline{\quad 8 \quad}$

$4 + 5 = \underline{\quad 9 \quad}$

$6 + 6 = \underline{\qquad}$

$6 + 7 = \underline{\qquad}$

$8 + 8 = \underline{\qquad}$

$8 + 9 = \underline{\qquad}$

$7 + 7 = \underline{\qquad}$

$7 + 8 = \underline{\qquad}$

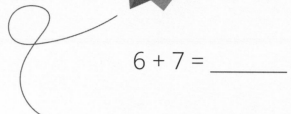

Add across.

3 + 4 = _____   6 + 7 = _____

5 + 6 = _____   7 + 8 = _____

4 + 5 = _____   8 + 9 = _____

Add down.

$$\begin{array}{r} 5 \\ +\,6 \\ \hline \end{array}\qquad\qquad \begin{array}{r} 6 \\ +\,7 \\ \hline \end{array}\qquad\qquad \begin{array}{r} 3 \\ +\,4 \\ \hline \end{array}$$

$$\begin{array}{r} 4 \\ +\,5 \\ \hline \end{array}\qquad\qquad \begin{array}{r} 7 \\ +\,8 \\ \hline \end{array}\qquad\qquad \begin{array}{r} 8 \\ +\,9 \\ \hline \end{array}$$

IXL.com
skill ID
XAY

You can also use doubles to help with doubles − 1. Add.

$5 + 5 =$ __10__

$5 + 4 =$ __9__

$9 + 9 =$ _____

$9 + 8 =$ _____

$6 + 6 =$ _____

$6 + 5 =$ _____

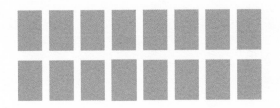

$8 + 8 =$ _____

$8 + 7 =$ _____

$7 + 7 =$ _____

$7 + 6 =$ _____

Add across.

5 + 4 = _____   6 + 5 = _____

4 + 3 = _____    7 + 6 = _____

8 + 7 = _____   9 + 8 = _____

Add down.

```
   4              6              9
 + 3            + 5            + 8
 ———            ———            ———
```

```
   5              7              8
 + 4            + 6            + 7
 ———            ———            ———
```

Write the missing numbers.

2 + __2__ = 4

2 + __3__ = 5

7 + _____ = 14

7 + _____ = 13

3 + _____ = 6

3 + _____ = 7

5 + _____ = 11

5 + _____ = 10

6 + _____ = 12

6 + _____ = 11

8 + _____ = 16

8 + _____ = 17

4 + _____ = 9

4 + _____ = 8

9 + _____ = 17

9 + _____ = 18

Add.

4 + 3	6 + 6	8 + 7
5 + 5	5 + 4	9 + 8
7 + 6	9 + 9	5 + 6
4 + 5	6 + 5	7 + 7

Find the path from start to finish! Follow the right answers to the end.

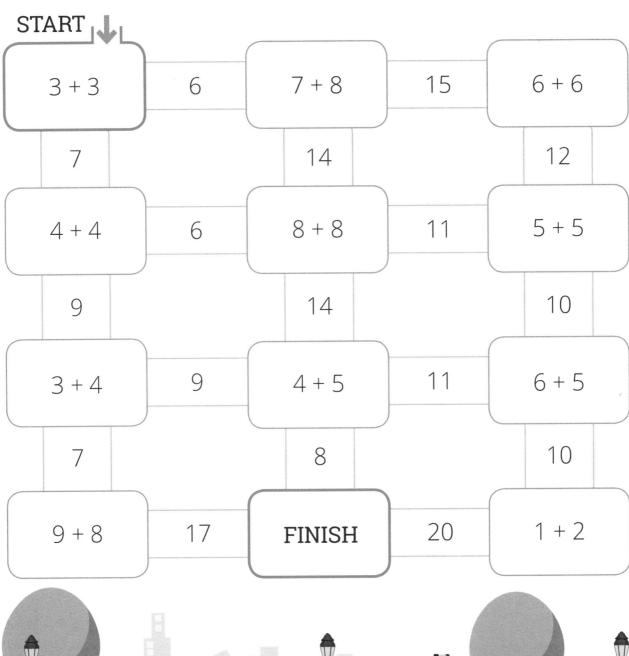

START

| 3 + 3 | 6 | 7 + 8 | 15 | 6 + 6 |

7   14   12

| 4 + 4 | 6 | 8 + 8 | 11 | 5 + 5 |

9   14   10

| 3 + 4 | 9 | 4 + 5 | 11 | 6 + 5 |

7   8   10

| 9 + 8 | 17 | FINISH | 20 | 1 + 2 |

Add across.

$10 + 2 = \underline{\ 12\ }$ $10 + 5 = \underline{\hspace{1cm}}$

$10 + 1 = \underline{\hspace{1cm}}$ $10 + 3 = \underline{\hspace{1cm}}$

$10 + 4 = \underline{\hspace{1cm}}$ $10 + 8 = \underline{\hspace{1cm}}$

Add down.

$$\begin{array}{r} 10 \\ +\ 6 \\ \hline \end{array} \qquad\qquad \begin{array}{r} 10 \\ +\ 9 \\ \hline \end{array}$$

$$\begin{array}{r} 10 \\ +\ 0 \\ \hline \end{array} \qquad\qquad \begin{array}{r} 10 \\ +\ 7 \\ \hline \end{array}$$

Let's Learn!

You can make a 10 to add. Use counters to help!

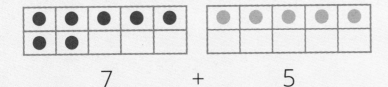

7   +   5

Show the problem with counters.

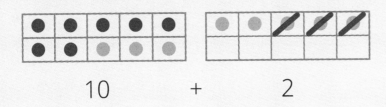

10   +   2

Move 3 orange counters to make a 10. There are 2 counters left over.

So, 7 + 5 is the same as 10 + 2. The sum is 12.

Make a 10. Then fill in the blanks to add.

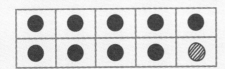   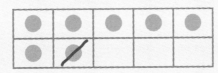

9 + 7 = ?

10 + __6__ = __16__

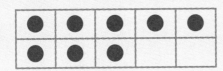   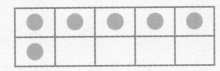

8 + 6 = ?

10 + ___ = ___

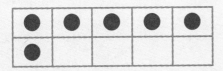   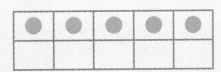

6 + 5 = ?

10 + ___ = ___

Keep going! Make a 10. Then fill in the blanks to add.

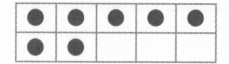

7 + 6 = ?

10 + ___ = ___

8 + 4 = ?

10 + ___ = ___

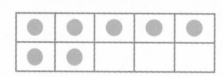

8 + 7 = ?

10 + ___ = ___

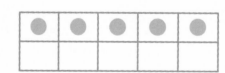

9 + 5 = ?

10 + ___ = ___

Make a 10. Fill in the blanks to add.

$6 + 9 = ?$

$10 + \underline{5} = \underline{15}$

$9 + 4 = ?$

$10 + \underline{} = \underline{}$

$7 + 8 = ?$

$10 + \underline{} = \underline{}$

$5 + 7 = ?$

$10 + \underline{} = \underline{}$

$8 + 3 = ?$

$10 + \underline{} = \underline{}$

$6 + 7 = ?$

$10 + \underline{} = \underline{}$

Add. Make a 10 to help!

$6 + 8 = \underline{14}$

$8 + 9 = \underline{}$

$9 + 3 = \underline{}$

$7 + 4 = \underline{}$

$8 + 5 = \underline{}$

$5 + 9 = \underline{}$

$7 + 9 = \underline{}$

$9 + 6 = \underline{}$

You can use a number line to add larger numbers, too! Add.

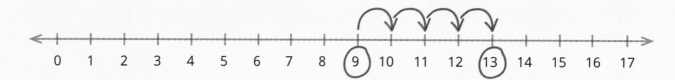

$9 + 4 = \underline{\quad 13 \quad}$

$9 + 6 = \underline{\qquad}$

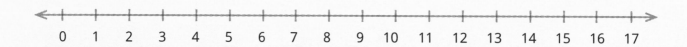

$11 + 4 = \underline{\qquad}$

$12 + 5 = \underline{\qquad}$

IXL.com
skill ID
LXW

Add.

$$\begin{array}{r} 6 \\ + 5 \\ \hline \end{array}$$
$$\begin{array}{r} 8 \\ + 4 \\ \hline \end{array}$$
$$\begin{array}{r} 7 \\ + 5 \\ \hline \end{array}$$

$$\begin{array}{r} 6 \\ + 7 \\ \hline \end{array}$$
$$\begin{array}{r} 8 \\ + 7 \\ \hline \end{array}$$
$$\begin{array}{r} 7 \\ + 7 \\ \hline \end{array}$$

$$\begin{array}{r} 6 \\ + 9 \\ \hline \end{array}$$
$$\begin{array}{r} 8 \\ + 9 \\ \hline \end{array}$$
$$\begin{array}{r} 9 \\ + 7 \\ \hline \end{array}$$

$$\begin{array}{r} 10 \\ + 3 \\ \hline \end{array}$$
$$\begin{array}{r} 12 \\ + 4 \\ \hline \end{array}$$
$$\begin{array}{r} 13 \\ + 5 \\ \hline \end{array}$$

IXL.com
skill ID
6TM

Add across and down to find the missing numbers.

1	+	7	=	8
+		+		+
6	+		=	8
=		=		=
7	+	9	=	

	+	2	=	6
+		+		+
1	+		=	6
=		=		=
5	+	7	=	

3	+	6	=	9
+		+		+
3	+	5	=	
=		=		=
	+		=	

	+	7	=	9
+		+		+
4	+		=	10
=		=		=
	+	13	=	

Answer each question.

A chipmunk hid 8 acorns in a hole. It hid 4 acorns in another hole. How many acorns did the chipmunk hide?

_____ acorns

Hannah borrowed 5 books from the library last month. She borrowed 6 books this month. How many books did Hannah borrow?

_____ books

There are 5 chickens inside the barn. There are 8 chickens in front of the barn. How many chickens are there in all?

_____ chickens

Bobby has 6 tickets for rides at the fair. Luke has 8 tickets for rides. How many tickets do they have in all?

_____ tickets

IXL.com
skill ID
KY5

Exploration Zone

RELATE ADDITION AND SUBTRACTION

You can use subtraction to undo addition! Try it with 3 + 4.

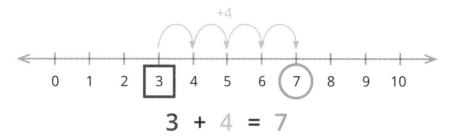

3 + 4 = 7

Start with 3 and add 4. The sum is 7.

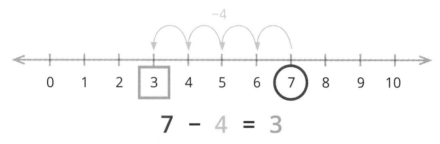

7 − 4 = 3

Next, start with 7 and *subtract* 4. Now you're back to 3!

IXL.com skill ID
DM2

TRY IT YOURSELF!

Fill in the blanks.

2 + 3 = 5

__5__ − __3__ = 2

4 + 5 = 9

____ − ____ = 4

12 + 4 = 16

____ − ____ = 12

5 + 2 = 7

____ − ____ = 5

Keep going! Fill in the blanks.

6 + 4 = 10   15 + 2 = 17

____ − ____ = 6   ____ − ____ = 15

Write + or − to complete each number sentence.

12 − 8 = 4   3 ☐ 7 = 10

4 ☐ 1 = 5   10 ☐ 2 = 8

5 ☐ 2 = 3   4 ☐ 3 = 7

2 ☐ 6 = 8   7 ☐ 2 = 9

14 ☐ 5 = 9

IXL.com
skill ID
7JY

Let's Learn!

3 + 1 + 2

4 + 2 = 6

You can add three numbers together! First, add two numbers. Then, add the last number.

Add.

2 + 5 + 1

__7__ + 1 = __8__

4 + 1 + 3

_____ + 3 = _____

2 + 4 + 3

_____ + 3 = _____

3 + 2 + 6

_____ + 6 = _____

6 + 3 + 1

_____ + 1 = _____

5 + 4 + 2

_____ + 2 = _____

Let's Learn!

You can pick any two numbers to add first. The answer is the same!

$$3 + 2 + 4$$
$$5 + 4 = 9$$

or

$$3 + 2 + 4$$
$$3 + 6 = 9$$

Add in two ways.

$$3 + 5 + 2$$
$$\underline{8} + 2 = \underline{10}$$

$$3 + 5 + 2$$
$$3 + \underline{7} = \underline{10}$$

$$7 + 3 + 1$$
$$\underline{} + 1 = \underline{}$$

$$7 + 3 + 1$$
$$7 + \underline{} = \underline{}$$

$$9 + 2 + 2$$
$$\underline{} + 2 = \underline{}$$

$$9 + 2 + 2$$
$$9 + \underline{} = \underline{}$$

$$2 + 4 + 6$$
$$\underline{} + 6 = \underline{}$$

$$2 + 4 + 6$$
$$2 + \underline{} = \underline{}$$

Add.

$4 + 4 + 3$

$\underline{\quad 8 \quad} + \underline{\quad 3 \quad} = \underline{\quad 11 \quad}$

$4 + 6 + 2$

$\underline{\qquad} + \underline{\qquad} = \underline{\qquad}$

$3 + 7 + 4$

$\underline{\qquad} + \underline{\qquad} = \underline{\qquad}$

$4 + 4 + 5$

$\underline{\qquad} + \underline{\qquad} = \underline{\qquad}$

$8 + 3 + 3$

$\underline{\qquad} + \underline{\qquad} = \underline{\qquad}$

$2 + 8 + 6$

$\underline{\qquad} + \underline{\qquad} = \underline{\qquad}$

$2 + 7 + 7$

$\underline{\qquad} + \underline{\qquad} = \underline{\qquad}$

$7 + 2 + 8$

$\underline{\qquad} + \underline{\qquad} = \underline{\qquad}$

$5 + 6 + 6$

$\underline{\qquad} + \underline{\qquad} = \underline{\qquad}$

IXL.com
skill ID
RL2

Add. Look for doubles or make a 10 to help!

$2 + 4 + 6 =$ ___12___
10

$3 + 3 + 5 =$ ___11___
6

$4 + 4 + 9 =$ _____

$5 + 2 + 8 =$ _____

$3 + 7 + 8 =$ _____

$8 + 8 + 3 =$ _____

$5 + 5 + 9 =$ _____

$3 + 6 + 6 =$ _____

$2 + 9 + 9 =$ _____

$6 + 4 + 7 =$ _____

Answer each question.

James has 2 dogs. His brother has 2 cats. His sister has 6 fish. How many pets do they have in all?

_____ pets

Kara is having a birthday party. She asked 3 friends to come. She also asked her 2 sisters and 3 cousins. How many people did she ask?

_____ people

Garrett works at the zoo and feeds animals. He fed 4 bears, 7 monkeys, and 2 lions. How many animals did he feed?

_____ animals

Kurt is writing thank-you cards. He wrote 4 cards before lunch. He wrote 5 cards after lunch. He wrote 6 cards the next day. How many thank-you cards did he write?

_____ cards

Mia, Abby, and Brian went shopping. The pictures show what each person bought. Use the pictures to answer each question.

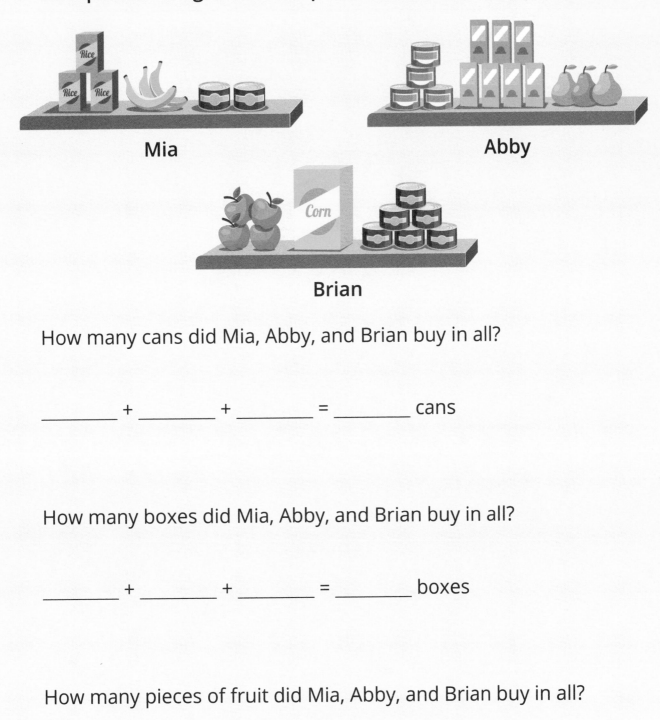

Mia

Abby

Brian

How many cans did Mia, Abby, and Brian buy in all?

_____ + _____ + _____ = _____ cans

How many boxes did Mia, Abby, and Brian buy in all?

_____ + _____ + _____ = _____ boxes

How many pieces of fruit did Mia, Abby, and Brian buy in all?

_____ + _____ + _____ = _____ pieces of fruit

Exploration Zone

PATTERNS

You can find patterns by adding! Look at this pattern.
To get the next number, you add 3.

3, 6, 9, 12, 15, 18

+3 +3 +3 +3 +3

TRY IT YOURSELF!

Find the pattern.

7, 14, 21, 28, 35   add _____

9, 18, 27, 36, 45   add _____

8, 16, 24, 32, 40   add _____

Find the pattern. Write the missing number.

5, 10, 15, ____, 25   add _____

4, 8, 12, ____, 20   add _____

6, 12, ____, 24, 30   add _____

INPUT/OUTPUT TABLES

You can use tables to show patterns. You put one number **in**. You use a rule to get another number **out**.

Rule: add 4		
In		**Out**
4	+ 4 →	8
5	+ 4 →	9
6	+ 4 →	10

IXL.com
skill ID
GLB

TRY IT YOURSELF!

Find the missing numbers.

Rule: add 5	
In	**Out**
4	9
5	10
6	11
7	
8	

Rule: add 3	
In	**Out**
5	8
6	
10	
11	14
17	

Let's Learn!

You can use blocks to add bigger numbers. Try it with 22 + 3! Count the blocks.

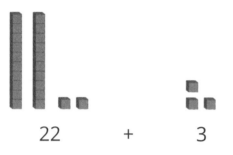

22   +   3

There are 2 tens blocks and 5 ones blocks.

So, 22 + 3 = 25.

Fill in the blanks to find the sum.

13 + 5 = ?

___1___ ten and ___8___ ones = ___18___

25 + 4 = ?

_____ tens and _____ ones = _____

32 + 6 = ?

_____ tens and _____ ones = _____

Add.

23 + 2 = ___25___

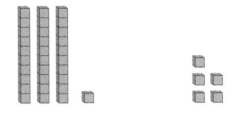

31 + 5 = _____

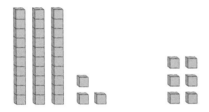

33 + 6 = _____

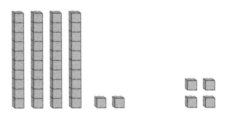

42 + 4 = _____

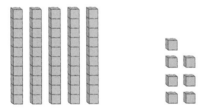

50 + 7 = _____

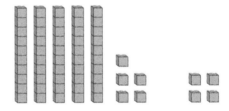

55 + 4 = _____

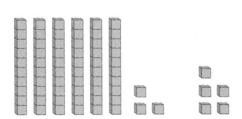

63 + 5 = _____

You can use blocks to add with tens, too! Fill in the blanks to find the sum.

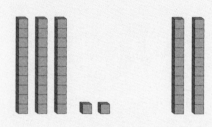

32 + 20 = ?

__5__ tens and __2__ ones = __52__

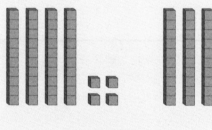

44 + 30 = ?

_____ tens and _____ ones = _____

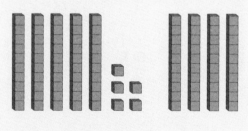

55 + 40 = ?

_____ tens and _____ ones = _____

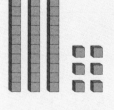 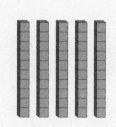

36 + 50 = ?

_____ tens and _____ ones = _____

Add.

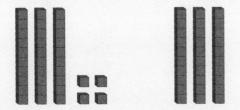

34 + 30 = _____

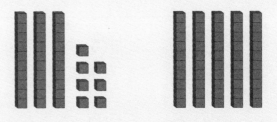

37 + 50 = _____

52 + 20 = _____

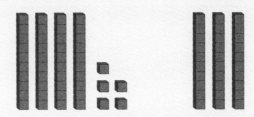

45 + 30 = _____

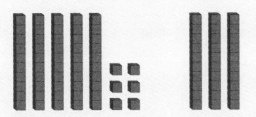

56 + 30 = _____

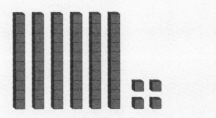

64 + 30 = _____

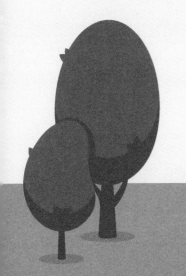

Add. Think about blocks to help!

28 + 10 = __38__   17 + 10 = _____

29 + 10 = _____   32 + 10 = _____

54 + 10 = _____   83 + 10 = _____

51 + 20 = _____   42 + 20 = _____

24 + 70 = _____   41 + 40 = _____

37 + 30 = _____   68 + 30 = _____

IXL.com
skill ID
LNL

You can use blocks to add both tens and ones. Fill in the blanks to find the sum.

__3__ tens and __7__ ones = __37__

25 + 12 = ?

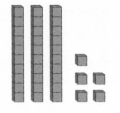 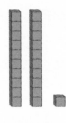

_____ tens and _____ ones = _____

35 + 21 = ?

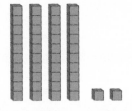 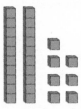

_____ tens and _____ ones = _____

42 + 27 = ?

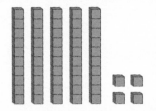 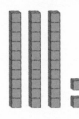

_____ tens and _____ ones = _____

54 + 33 = ?

Add.

34 + 13 = _____   25 + 24 = _____

33 + 33 = _____   31 + 27 = _____

56 + 23 = _____   74 + 11 = _____

Time to review! Add. Think about blocks to help.

40 + 5 = _____   22 + 6 = _____

36 + 3 = _____   46 + 3 = _____

62 + 2 = _____   83 + 5 = _____

42 + 25 = _____   34 + 14 = _____

25 + 34 = _____   60 + 23 = _____

72 + 25 = _____   63 + 36 = _____

Let's Learn!

You can make a ten to help with harder problems. Try it with 16 + 8!

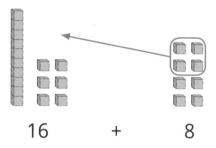

16 + 8

Move 4 ones blocks over to make a ten.

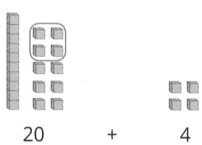

20 + 4

There are **2** tens and **4** ones. So, the sum is 24.

Move the ones blocks to make a ten. Then fill in the blanks to find the sum.

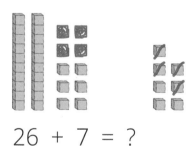

26 + 7 = ?

__3__ tens and __3__ ones = __33__

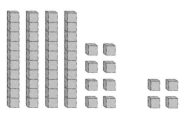

48 + 4 = ?

_____ tens and _____ ones = _____

Move the ones blocks to make a ten. Then fill in the blanks to find the sum.

38 + 3 = ?

_____ tens and _____ one = _____

45 + 8 = ?

_____ tens and _____ ones = _____

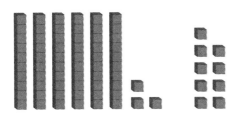

63 + 9 = ?

_____ tens and _____ ones = _____

For more practice, visit IXL.com or the IXL mobile app and enter this code in the search bar.

IXL.com
skill ID
8RL

Move the ones blocks to make a ten. Then find the sum.

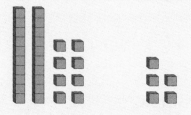

28 + 5 = _____

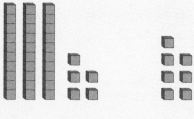

35 + 7 = _____

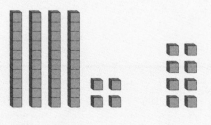

44 + 8 = _____

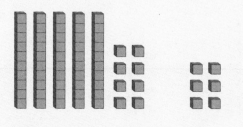

58 + 6 = _____

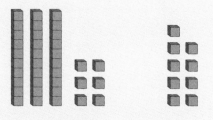

36 + 9 = _____

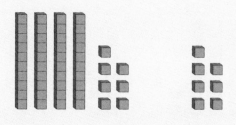

47 + 7 = _____

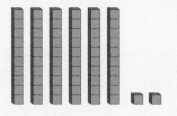

62 + 9 = _____

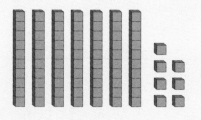
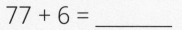

77 + 6 = _____

Let's Learn!

You can use place value to add. Try it with 24 + 3.

$$
\begin{array}{r}
2\ \overline{4} \\
+\ \ \ 3 \\
\hline
7
\end{array}
$$

$4 + 3 = 7$

First, line up the numbers.

Then, add all the **ones**.

$$
\begin{array}{r}
\overline{2}\ 4 \\
+\ \ \ 3 \\
\hline
2\ 7
\end{array}
$$

Now, bring down the **tens**.

The number below the line is the answer! So, 24 + 3 = 27.

Add.

$$
\begin{array}{r}
2\ 5 \\
+\ \ \ 4 \\
\hline
2\ 9
\end{array}
\qquad
\begin{array}{r}
4\ 2 \\
+\ \ \ 5 \\
\hline
\end{array}
\qquad
\begin{array}{r}
3\ 1 \\
+\ \ \ 5 \\
\hline
\end{array}
$$

$$
\begin{array}{r}
5\ 4 \\
+\ \ \ 4 \\
\hline
\end{array}
\qquad
\begin{array}{r}
6\ 2 \\
+\ \ \ 3 \\
\hline
\end{array}
\qquad
\begin{array}{r}
7\ 5 \\
+\ \ \ 3 \\
\hline
\end{array}
$$

Keep going! Add.

$$
\begin{array}{r}
40 \\
+\ 8 \\
\hline
\end{array}
\qquad
\begin{array}{r}
35 \\
+\ 2 \\
\hline
\end{array}
\qquad
\begin{array}{r}
22 \\
+\ 6 \\
\hline
\end{array}
$$

$$
\begin{array}{r}
42 \\
+\ 4 \\
\hline
\end{array}
\qquad
\begin{array}{r}
26 \\
+\ 3 \\
\hline
\end{array}
\qquad
\begin{array}{r}
32 \\
+\ 7 \\
\hline
\end{array}
$$

$$
\begin{array}{r}
56 \\
+\ 2 \\
\hline
\end{array}
\qquad
\begin{array}{r}
71 \\
+\ 8 \\
\hline
\end{array}
\qquad
\begin{array}{r}
63 \\
+\ 4 \\
\hline
\end{array}
$$

$$
\begin{array}{r}
83 \\
+\ 3 \\
\hline
\end{array}
\qquad
\begin{array}{r}
90 \\
+\ 7 \\
\hline
\end{array}
\qquad
\begin{array}{r}
94 \\
+\ 5 \\
\hline
\end{array}
$$

IXL.com
skill ID
5VX

Let's Learn!

When you use place value to add, you may need to regroup. Try it with 45 + 7.

$$\begin{array}{r} \overset{1}{4\,5} \\ +\ \ 7 \\ \hline 2 \end{array}$$

$5 + 7 = 12$

When you add the **ones**, you get 12. Remember, 12 has 1 ten and 2 ones. So, you need to regroup!

Write the 2 below the ones. Write the 1 above the tens.

$$\begin{array}{r} \overset{1}{4\,5} \\ +\ \ 7 \\ \hline 5\,2 \end{array}$$

$1 + 4 = 5$

Now, add the **tens**. Add the 4 to the 1 you regrouped.

So, 45 + 7 = 52.

Add.

$$\begin{array}{r} \overset{1}{2\,6} \\ +\ \ 5 \\ \hline 3\,1 \end{array} \qquad \begin{array}{r} 4\,3 \\ +\ \ 9 \\ \hline \end{array} \qquad \begin{array}{r} 3\,8 \\ +\ \ 8 \\ \hline \end{array}$$

Keep going! Add.

$$\begin{array}{r} 16 \\ +8 \\ \hline \end{array}$$

$$\begin{array}{r} 28 \\ +5 \\ \hline \end{array}$$

$$\begin{array}{r} 23 \\ +8 \\ \hline \end{array}$$

$$\begin{array}{r} 19 \\ +6 \\ \hline \end{array}$$

$$\begin{array}{r} 37 \\ +5 \\ \hline \end{array}$$

$$\begin{array}{r} 46 \\ +4 \\ \hline \end{array}$$

$$\begin{array}{r} 59 \\ +2 \\ \hline \end{array}$$

$$\begin{array}{r} 48 \\ +7 \\ \hline \end{array}$$

$$\begin{array}{r} 74 \\ +8 \\ \hline \end{array}$$

$$\begin{array}{r} 83 \\ +7 \\ \hline \end{array}$$

$$\begin{array}{r} 82 \\ +9 \\ \hline \end{array}$$

$$\begin{array}{r} 65 \\ +8 \\ \hline \end{array}$$

Fill in the missing number.

```
   4 6              3 6              □ 3
 +  [2]           +   3            +  3
 ─────            ─────            ─────
   4 8              □ 9              8 6
```

```
   4 8              2 6              7 7
 +  5             +  □             +  6
 ─────            ─────            ─────
   □ 3              3 2              8 □
```

```
   5 □              8 □              7 2
 +  8             +  8             +  □
 ─────            ─────            ─────
   6 0              9 6              8 1
```

Let's Learn!

Follow similar steps to add two bigger numbers. Try it with 36 + 17. Regroup if you need to!

$$\begin{array}{r} \overset{1}{3}6 \\ + 1\,7 \\ \hline 3 \end{array}$$

$$\begin{array}{r} \overset{1}{3}6 \\ + 1\,7 \\ \hline 5\,3 \end{array}$$

6 + 7 = 13   1 + 3 + 1 = 5

Add.

$$\begin{array}{r} 1\,4 \\ + 1\,5 \\ \hline 2\,9 \end{array}$$

$$\begin{array}{r} 4\,5 \\ + 2\,3 \\ \hline \end{array}$$

$$\begin{array}{r} 3\,9 \\ + 1\,5 \\ \hline \end{array}$$

$$\begin{array}{r} 2\,9 \\ + 1\,9 \\ \hline \end{array}$$

$$\begin{array}{r} 4\,3 \\ + 2\,6 \\ \hline \end{array}$$

$$\begin{array}{r} 3\,8 \\ + 3\,4 \\ \hline \end{array}$$

IXL.com
skill ID
GLX

Keep going! Add.

$$\begin{array}{r} 26 \\ +14 \\ \hline \end{array}$$
$$\begin{array}{r} 38 \\ +15 \\ \hline \end{array}$$
$$\begin{array}{r} 22 \\ +36 \\ \hline \end{array}$$

$$\begin{array}{r} 21 \\ +39 \\ \hline \end{array}$$
$$\begin{array}{r} 38 \\ +38 \\ \hline \end{array}$$
$$\begin{array}{r} 42 \\ +23 \\ \hline \end{array}$$

$$\begin{array}{r} 64 \\ +13 \\ \hline \end{array}$$
$$\begin{array}{r} 26 \\ +55 \\ \hline \end{array}$$
$$\begin{array}{r} 27 \\ +45 \\ \hline \end{array}$$

$$\begin{array}{r} 77 \\ +12 \\ \hline \end{array}$$
$$\begin{array}{r} 27 \\ +53 \\ \hline \end{array}$$
$$\begin{array}{r} 56 \\ +38 \\ \hline \end{array}$$

Troy, James, and Alice are shopping for their family trip to the beach. Use the picture to answer each question.

Troy wants to buy a swimsuit and a bucket. How much money will he need?

$_____ + \$_____ = \$_____

James wants to buy a beach towel and a beach ball. How much money will he need?

$_____ + \$_____ = \$_____

Alice wants to buy a beach bag and water bottle. How much money will she need?

$_____ + \$_____ = \$_____

IXL.com
skill ID
5LZ

Add each block to the block next to it. The sum goes above!

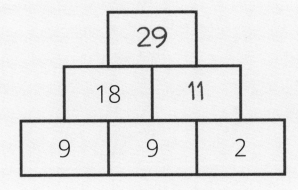

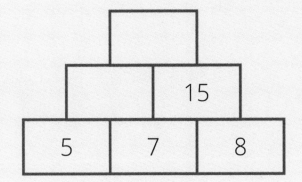

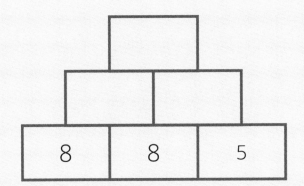

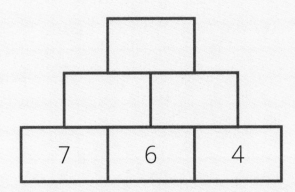

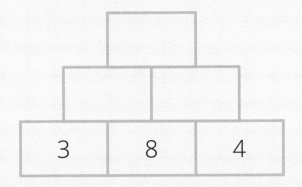

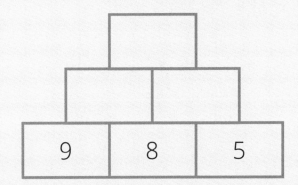

Review your addition facts. Try to be quick!

7 + 3 = _____   2 + 4 = _____

1 + 6 = _____   0 + 3 = _____

4 + 5 = _____   5 + 2 = _____

10 + 0 = _____   3 + 3 = _____

Keep going! How fast can you add?

$$\begin{array}{r} 6 \\ + 2 \\ \hline \end{array} \qquad \begin{array}{r} 8 \\ + 1 \\ \hline \end{array} \qquad \begin{array}{r} 3 \\ + 5 \\ \hline \end{array}$$

$$\begin{array}{r} 4 \\ + 0 \\ \hline \end{array} \qquad \begin{array}{r} 3 \\ + 2 \\ \hline \end{array} \qquad \begin{array}{r} 8 \\ + 2 \\ \hline \end{array}$$

$$\begin{array}{r} 4 \\ + 4 \\ \hline \end{array} \qquad \begin{array}{r} 2 \\ + 7 \\ \hline \end{array} \qquad \begin{array}{r} 6 \\ + 3 \\ \hline \end{array}$$

Circle pairs of numbers that add to 10! You can add in any direction.

2	9	10	0	2	7
4	1	3	8	5	3
2	7	4	6	5	10
8	7	10	8	9	1
5	3	9	6	4	7
4	5	1	0	3	5

LOOK AGAIN! | How many pairs did you find? See if you can find all 14!

Write the doubles fact that equals the sum at the bottom.

Add across.

9 + 4 = _____  8 + 3 = _____

6 + 6 = _____ 7 + 5 = _____

5 + 9 = _____ 6 + 8 = _____

9 + 2 = _____ 8 + 8 = _____

Add down.

$$\begin{array}{r} 6 \\ + 7 \\ \hline \end{array}$$
$$\begin{array}{r} 5 \\ + 8 \\ \hline \end{array}$$
$$\begin{array}{r} 9 \\ + 9 \\ \hline \end{array}$$

$$\begin{array}{r} 5 \\ + 6 \\ \hline \end{array}$$
$$\begin{array}{r} 4 \\ + 9 \\ \hline \end{array}$$
$$\begin{array}{r} 8 \\ + 9 \\ \hline \end{array}$$

$$\begin{array}{r} 8 \\ + 4 \\ \hline \end{array}$$
$$\begin{array}{r} 9 \\ + 7 \\ \hline \end{array}$$
$$\begin{array}{r} 7 \\ + 8 \\ \hline \end{array}$$

IXL.com
skill ID
XWH

Use the numbers to fill in the blanks. Use each number once.

2, 3, 7, 9

__3__ + __7__ = 10

__2__ + __9__ = 11

4, 5, 7, 8

_____ + _____ = 11

_____ + _____ = 13

1, 6, 8, 9

_____ + _____ = 10

_____ + _____ = 14

4, 5, 7, 9

_____ + _____ = 12

_____ + _____ = 13

6, 7, 8, 9

_____ + _____ = 13

_____ + _____ = 17

3, 4, 7, 9

_____ + _____ = 11

_____ + _____ = 12

IXL.com
skill ID
UMX

Use the numbers in the box to balance the scale. Both sides should equal the sum in the middle!

| 3̸ | 4̸ | 5̸ | 6̸ |

3 + 6 = 4 + 5

sum
9

| 5 6 7 8 |

☐ + ☐ = ☐ + ☐

sum
13

| 6 7 8 9 |

☐ + ☐ = ☐ + ☐

sum
15

| 7 6 7 8 |

☐ + ☐ = ☐ + ☐

sum
14

IXL.com
skill ID
6LC

Find each sum.

4 + 6 + 3 = _____   5 + 5 + 8 = _____

5 + 6 + 9 = _____   7 + 3 + 4 = _____

6 + 6 + 3 = _____   5 + 7 + 8 = _____

Challenge yourself! Write three numbers that make each sum.

__3__ + __2__ + __5__ = 10

_____ + _____ + _____ = 12

_____ + _____ + _____ = 15

_____ + _____ + _____ = 20

Answer each question.

Oliver is buying lunch. He buys milk for $2, an apple for $1, and a hot dog for $4. How much money is that in all?

$_____

Sweet Street Bakery made 5 carrot cakes and 4 lemon cakes. It also made 4 apple pies and 3 pumpkin pies. Did the bakery make more cakes or pies?

_____

James went to the zoo. He saw 3 lions, 7 monkeys, and 4 bears. How many animals did he see in all?

_____ animals

Amy has 5 red bracelets and 7 purple bracelets. Brenda has 6 pink bracelets and 8 yellow bracelets. Who has more bracelets?

_____

Add.

$$
\begin{array}{r}
15 \\
+\ \ 4 \\
\hline
\end{array}
\qquad
\begin{array}{r}
28 \\
+\ \ 3 \\
\hline
\end{array}
\qquad
\begin{array}{r}
22 \\
+\ \ 7 \\
\hline
\end{array}
$$

$$
\begin{array}{r}
19 \\
+\ \ 9 \\
\hline
\end{array}
\qquad
\begin{array}{r}
31 \\
+\ \ 6 \\
\hline
\end{array}
\qquad
\begin{array}{r}
44 \\
+\ \ 8 \\
\hline
\end{array}
$$

$$
\begin{array}{r}
45 \\
+\ \ 3 \\
\hline
\end{array}
\qquad
\begin{array}{r}
56 \\
+\ \ 2 \\
\hline
\end{array}
\qquad
\begin{array}{r}
72 \\
+\ \ 9 \\
\hline
\end{array}
$$

$$
\begin{array}{r}
85 \\
+\ \ 5 \\
\hline
\end{array}
\qquad
\begin{array}{r}
69 \\
+\ \ 4 \\
\hline
\end{array}
\qquad
\begin{array}{r}
76 \\
+\ \ 5 \\
\hline
\end{array}
$$

Find the line where all the sums are the same.

35 +13 48	21 +15 36	24 +13 37
36 + 6 42	42 + 6 48	49 +10 59
33 +14 47	24 + 4 28	39 + 9 48

43 + 8	34 +32	52 +17
71 +12	62 + 6	29 +12
61 + 4	58 + 7	32 +33

Maria and her friends are at a yard sale. Use the picture to answer each question.

Maria wants to buy the doll and a bouncy ball. How much money will she need?

_____ cents

Dan wants to buy 2 books. How much money will he need?

_____ cents

Keep going! Use the picture to answer each question.

Justin wants to buy a teddy bear and 2 bouncy balls. How much money will he need?

_____ cents

Jeff has 85 cents. He wants to buy a book and the race car. Will he need more than 85 cents?

_____

Amy has 90 cents. She wants to buy the bell and picnic basket. Will she need more than 90 cents?

_____

PAGE 2

2 leaves and 2 leaves is 4 leaves.
4 cupcakes and 3 cupcakes is 7 cupcakes.
1 duck and 4 ducks is 5 ducks.

PAGE 3

1 puzzle piece and 8 puzzle pieces is 9 puzzle pieces.
3 butterflies and 2 butterflies is 5 butterflies.
5 ice pops and 5 ice pops is 10 ice pops.

PAGE 4

4 horses and 6 horses is 10 horses.
2 hamsters and 6 hamsters is 8 hamsters.
4 cows and 4 cows is 8 cows.

PAGE 5

3 sandwiches plus 5 sandwiches equals 8 sandwiches.
4 crackers plus 2 crackers equals 6 crackers.
1 ant plus 6 ants equals 7 ants.

PAGE 6

2 coins plus 3 coins equals 5 coins.
1 nest plus 3 nests equals 4 nests.
4 snowballs plus 2 snowballs equals 6 snowballs.

PAGE 7

4 pies plus 5 pies equals 9 pies.
3 books plus 3 books equals 6 books.
3 hats plus 4 hats equals 7 hats.

PAGE 8

$3 \oplus 2 \ominus 5$
$4 \oplus 4 \ominus 8$

PAGE 9

$1 \oplus 5 \ominus 6$
$5 + 2 = 7$ $2 + 2 = 4$
$3 + 6 = 9$ $1 + 8 = 9$

PAGE 10

$2 + 2 = 4$
$3 + 2 = 5$
$2 + 1 = 3$
$3 + 3 = 6$

PAGE 11

$4 + 4 = 8$ children
$3 + 3 = 6$ dogs
$8 + 2 = 10$ animals
$2 + 3 = 5$ friends

PAGE 12

PAGE 13

$2 + 5 = 7$
$3 + 2 = 5$
$6 + 4 = 10$
$5 + 3 = 8$

PAGE 14

$4 + 3 = 7$
$1 + 4 = 5$
$4 + 5 = 9$
$2 + 6 = 8$

PAGE 15

$3 + 1 = 4$	$2 + 3 = 5$
$1 + 4 = 5$	$1 + 3 = 4$
$2 + 2 = 4$	$4 + 1 = 5$
$3 + 2 = 5$	$2 + 2 = 4$

PAGE 16

$1 + 3 = 4$	$2 + 2 = 4$
$2 + 3 = 5$	$3 + 1 = 4$
$1 + 4 = 5$	$3 + 2 = 5$

PAGE 16, continued

$2 + 3 = 5$	$3 + 1 = 4$
$4 + 1 = 5$	$2 + 2 = 4$
$1 + 3 = 4$	$3 + 2 = 5$

PAGE 17

$4 + 0 = 4$	$0 + 3 = 3$
$0 + 5 = 5$	$2 + 0 = 2$
$0 + 4 = 4$	

PAGE 18

$3 + 1 = 4$	$1 + 0 = 1$
$2 + 2 = 4$	$1 + 1 = 2$
$5 + 0 = 5$	$3 + 2 = 5$
$1 + 2 = 3$	$4 + 1 = 5$
$1 + 3 = 4$	$0 + 2 = 2$

PAGE 19

$2 + 4 = 6$	$3 + 4 = 7$
$5 + 2 = 7$	$5 + 1 = 6$
$3 + 3 = 6$	$4 + 3 = 7$
$6 + 1 = 7$	$1 + 5 = 6$

PAGE 20

$1 + 5 = 6$	$3 + 4 = 7$
$3 + 2 = 5$	$2 + 1 = 3$
$5 + 2 = 7$	$3 + 3 = 6$
$1 + 6 = 7$	$3 + 0 = 3$
$4 + 1 = 5$	$2 + 4 = 6$

PAGE 21

$4 + 5 = 9$	$2 + 6 = 8$
$1 + 7 = 8$	$3 + 6 = 9$
$2 + 7 = 9$	$3 + 5 = 8$
$4 + 4 = 8$	$8 + 1 = 9$

PAGE 22

$2 + 7 = 9$	$3 + 5 = 8$
$6 + 1 = 7$	$4 + 2 = 6$
$6 + 2 = 8$	$3 + 6 = 9$
$1 + 7 = 8$	$1 + 3 = 4$
$2 + 2 = 4$	$0 + 4 = 4$
$2 + 5 = 7$	$4 + 4 = 8$
$4 + 1 = 5$	$5 + 4 = 9$

PAGE 23

1 + 5 = 6	0 + 7 = 7
2 + 3 = 5	6 + 3 = 9
1 + 2 = 3	3 + 3 = 6
2 + 6 = 8	1 + 4 = 5
9 + 0 = 9	7 + 1 = 8
3 + 4 = 7	4 + 5 = 9

PAGE 24

3 + 3 = 6	2 + 5 = 7
1 + 4 = 5	8 + 0 = 8
3 + 6 = 9	6 + 1 = 7
4 + 4 = 8	5 + 4 = 9
2 + 7 = 9	7 + 1 = 8

PAGE 25

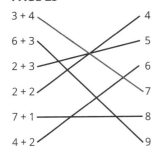

3 + 4 — 4
6 + 3 — 5
2 + 3 — 6
2 + 2 — 7
7 + 1 — 8
4 + 2 — 9

PAGE 26

3 + 4 = 7 flowers
2 + 6 = 8 fruit snacks
2 + 5 = 7 books
4 + 5 = 9 squirrels

PAGE 27

4 + 6 = 10
7 + 3 = 10
2 + 8 = 10

PAGE 28

5 + 5 = 10	2 + 8 = 10
1 + 9 = 10	6 + 4 = 10
7 + 3 = 10	8 + 2 = 10

PAGE 29

3 + 7 = 10   5 + 5 = 10

9 + 1 = 10   4 + 6 = 10

Answers may vary. Some possible answers are shown below.

7 + 3 = 10   8 + 2 = 10

PAGE 30

6 + 4 = 10	5 + 5 = 10
3 + 7 = 10	8 + 2 = 10
9 + 1 = 10	4 + 6 = 10
7 + 3 = 10	2 + 8 = 10
0 + 10 = 10	1 + 9 = 10

PAGE 31

Order of answers may vary.

1 + 9 = 10	6 + 4 = 10
0 + 10 = 10	7 + 3 = 10
2 + 8 = 10	8 + 2 = 10
3 + 7 = 10	9 + 1 = 10
4 + 6 = 10	10 + 0 = 10
5 + 5 = 10	

PAGE 32

10 bouncy balls
10 party hats
5 lollipops

PAGE 33

START ↓

3 + 7	1 + 9	2 + 3
3 + 5	2 + 8	3 + 3
1 + 5	5 + 5	4 + 6
2 + 6	4 + 4	9 + 1
2 + 7	6 + 3	7 + 3

FINISH ↓

PAGE 34

5 baby goats
4 baby sheep
baby goats
9 baby animals

PAGE 35

3 hot dogs
5 boxes
4 trays

PAGE 36

4 friends
3 friends
7 friends

PAGE 37

blue
2 friends
7 friends
9 friends

PAGE 38

2 + 1 = 3	1 + 2 = 3
2 + 3 = 5	3 + 2 = 5
3 + 5 = 8	5 + 3 = 8

No. When you change the order of numbers in an addition sentence, the sum is still the same.

PAGE 39

3 + 4 = 7	2 + 7 = 9
4 + 3 = 7	7 + 2 = 9
1 + 5 = 6	2 + 8 = 10
5 + 1 = 6	8 + 2 = 10
6 + 2 = 8	2 + 5 = 7
2 + 6 = 8	5 + 2 = 7
6 + 3 = 9	7 + 3 = 10
3 + 6 = 9	3 + 7 = 10
9 + 1 = 10	4 + 5 = 9
1 + 9 = 10	5 + 4 = 9

PAGE 40

4 + 3 = 5 + 2

2 + 6 = 4 + 4

4 + 6 = 7 + 3

PAGE 41

5 + 2 = 3 + 4   2 + 3 = 1 + 4

5 + 4 = 2 + 7   2 + 8 = 4 + 6

3 + 3 = 5 + 1   5 + 5 = 6 + 4

Answers may vary. Some possible answers are shown below.

4 + 4 = 2 + 6   6 + 3 = 7 + 2

1 + 4 = 3 + 2   2 + 5 = 3 + 4

2 + 4 = 3 + 3   1 + 9 = 4 + 6

PAGE 42

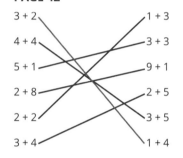

3 + 2   1 + 3
4 + 4   3 + 3
5 + 1   9 + 1
2 + 8   2 + 5
2 + 2   3 + 5
3 + 4   1 + 4

PAGE 43

6 + 1 = 7

$$\begin{array}{r} 6 \\ + 1 \\ \hline 7 \end{array}$$

2 + 4 = 6

$$\begin{array}{r} 2 \\ + 4 \\ \hline 6 \end{array}$$

5 + 3 = 8

$$\begin{array}{r} 5 \\ + 3 \\ \hline 8 \end{array}$$

PAGE 44

3 + 7 = 10   3 + 4 = 7

$$\begin{array}{r} 3 \\ + 7 \\ \hline 10 \end{array}$$ $$\begin{array}{r} 3 \\ + 4 \\ \hline 7 \end{array}$$

5 + 2 = 7   1 + 8 = 9

$$\begin{array}{r} 5 \\ + 2 \\ \hline 7 \end{array}$$ $$\begin{array}{r} 1 \\ + 8 \\ \hline 9 \end{array}$$

PAGE 45

$$\begin{array}{r} 2 \\ + 5 \\ \hline 7 \end{array}$$ $$\begin{array}{r} 3 \\ + 2 \\ \hline 5 \end{array}$$ $$\begin{array}{r} 7 \\ + 2 \\ \hline 9 \end{array}$$

$$\begin{array}{r} 3 \\ + 3 \\ \hline 6 \end{array}$$ $$\begin{array}{r} 6 \\ + 2 \\ \hline 8 \end{array}$$ $$\begin{array}{r} 4 \\ + 6 \\ \hline 10 \end{array}$$

$$\begin{array}{r} 1 \\ + 3 \\ \hline 4 \end{array}$$ $$\begin{array}{r} 5 \\ + 1 \\ \hline 6 \end{array}$$ $$\begin{array}{r} 4 \\ + 4 \\ \hline 8 \end{array}$$

$$\begin{array}{r} 0 \\ + 7 \\ \hline 7 \end{array}$$ $$\begin{array}{r} 7 \\ + 3 \\ \hline 10 \end{array}$$ $$\begin{array}{r} 5 \\ + 4 \\ \hline 9 \end{array}$$

PAGE 46

3 + 3 = 6   5 + 5 = 10

4 + 4 = 8   6 + 6 = 12

8 + 8 = 16   7 + 7 = 14

PAGE 47

4 + 4 = 8   5 + 5 = 10

6 + 6 = 12   3 + 3 = 6

8 + 8 = 16   9 + 9 = 18

$$\begin{array}{r} 4 \\ + 4 \\ \hline 8 \end{array}$$ $$\begin{array}{r} 7 \\ + 7 \\ \hline 14 \end{array}$$ $$\begin{array}{r} 8 \\ + 8 \\ \hline 16 \end{array}$$

PAGE 48

8 cards

12 kites

10 trains

6 legs

PAGE 49

4 + 4 = 8

4 + 5 = 9

6 + 6 = 12

6 + 7 = 13

8 + 8 = 16

8 + 9 = 17

7 + 7 = 14

7 + 8 = 15

PAGE 50

3 + 4 = 7   6 + 7 = 13

5 + 6 = 11   7 + 8 = 15

4 + 5 = 9   8 + 9 = 17

$$\begin{array}{r} 5 \\ + 6 \\ \hline 11 \end{array}$$ $$\begin{array}{r} 6 \\ + 7 \\ \hline 13 \end{array}$$ $$\begin{array}{r} 3 \\ + 4 \\ \hline 7 \end{array}$$

$$\begin{array}{r} 4 \\ + 5 \\ \hline 9 \end{array}$$ $$\begin{array}{r} 7 \\ + 8 \\ \hline 15 \end{array}$$ $$\begin{array}{r} 8 \\ + 9 \\ \hline 17 \end{array}$$

PAGE 51

5 + 5 = 10

5 + 4 = 9

9 + 9 = 18

9 + 8 = 17

6 + 6 = 12

6 + 5 = 11

8 + 8 = 16

8 + 7 = 15

7 + 7 = 14

7 + 6 = 13

PAGE 52

5 + 4 = 9   6 + 5 = 11

4 + 3 = 7   7 + 6 = 13

8 + 7 = 15   9 + 8 = 17

$$\begin{array}{r} 4 \\ + 3 \\ \hline 7 \end{array}$$ $$\begin{array}{r} 6 \\ + 5 \\ \hline 11 \end{array}$$ $$\begin{array}{r} 9 \\ + 8 \\ \hline 17 \end{array}$$

$$\begin{array}{r} 5 \\ + 4 \\ \hline 9 \end{array}$$ $$\begin{array}{r} 7 \\ + 6 \\ \hline 13 \end{array}$$ $$\begin{array}{r} 8 \\ + 7 \\ \hline 15 \end{array}$$

PAGE 53

2 + 2 = 4   6 + 6 = 12

2 + 3 = 5   6 + 5 = 11

7 + 7 = 14   8 + 8 = 16

7 + 6 = 13   8 + 9 = 17

PAGE 53, *continued*

3 + 3 = 6   4 + 5 = 9
3 + 4 = 7   4 + 4 = 8

5 + 6 = 11   9 + 8 = 17
5 + 5 = 10   9 + 9 = 18

PAGE 54

4	6	8
+ 3	+ 6	+ 7
7	12	15

5	5	9
+ 5	+ 4	+ 8
10	9	17

7	9	5
+ 6	+ 9	+ 6
13	18	11

4	6	7
+ 5	+ 5	+ 7
9	11	14

PAGE 55

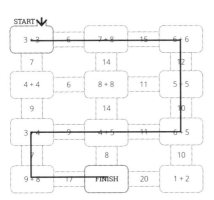

PAGE 56

10 + 2 = 12   10 + 5 = 15
10 + 1 = 11   10 + 3 = 13
10 + 4 = 14   10 + 8 = 18

10	10
+ 6	+ 9
16	19

10	10
+ 0	+ 7
10	17

PAGE 57

10 + 6 = 16

PAGE 57, *continued*

10 + 4 = 14

10 + 1 = 11

PAGE 58

10 + 3 = 13

10 + 2 = 12

10 + 5 = 15

10 + 4 = 14

PAGE 59

6 + 9 = ?   9 + 4 = ?
10 + 5 = 15   10 + 3 = 13

7 + 8 = ?   5 + 7 = ?
10 + 5 = 15   10 + 2 = 12

8 + 3 = ?   6 + 7 = ?
10 + 1 = 11   10 + 3 = 13

6 + 8 = 14   8 + 9 = 17
9 + 3 = 12   7 + 4 = 11
8 + 5 = 13   5 + 9 = 14
7 + 9 = 16   9 + 6 = 15

PAGE 60

9 + 4 = 13
9 + 6 = 15
11 + 4 = 15
12 + 5 = 17

PAGE 61

6	8	7
+ 5	+ 4	+ 5
11	12	12

6	8	7
+ 7	+ 7	+ 7
13	15	14

PAGE 61, *continued*

6	8	9
+ 9	+ 9	+ 7
15	17	16

10	12	13
+ 3	+ 4	+ 5
13	16	18

PAGE 62

1	+	7	=	8
+		+		+
6	+	2	=	8
=		=		=
7	+	9	=	16

4	+	2	=	6
+		+		+
1	+	5	=	6
=		=		=
5	+	7	=	12

3	+	6	=	9
+		+		+
3	+	5	=	8
=		=		=
6	+	11	=	17

2	+	7	=	9
+		+		+
4	+	6	=	10
=		=		=
6	+	13	=	19

PAGE 63

12 acorns
11 books
13 chickens
14 tickets

PAGE 64

5 − 3 = 2   9 − 5 = 4
16 − 4 = 12   7 − 2 = 5

PAGE 65

10 − 4 = 6   17 − 2 = 15

12 − 8 = 4   3 + 7 = 10
4 + 1 = 5   10 − 2 = 8
5 − 2 = 3   4 + 3 = 7
2 + 6 = 8   7 + 2 = 9
14 − 5 = 9

PAGE 66

2 + 5 + 1 = 7 + 1 = 8   4 + 1 + 3 = 5 + 3 = 8
2 + 4 + 3 = 6 + 3 = 9   3 + 2 + 6 = 5 + 6 = 11
6 + 3 + 1 = 9 + 1 = 10   5 + 4 + 2 = 9 + 2 = 11

PAGE 67

3 + 5 + 2 = 8 + 2 = 10   3 + 5 + 2 = 3 + 7 = 10
7 + 3 + 1 = 10 + 1 = 11   7 + 3 + 1 = 7 + 4 = 11
9 + 2 + 2 = 11 + 2 = 13   9 + 2 + 2 = 9 + 4 = 13
2 + 4 + 6 = 6 + 6 = 12   2 + 4 + 6 = 2 + 10 = 12

PAGE 68

Combinations may vary. Some possible combinations are shown below.

4 + 4 + 3 = 8 + 3 = 11   4 + 6 + 2 = 10 + 2 = 12

3 + 7 + 4 = 10 + 4 = 14   4 + 4 + 5 = 8 + 5 = 13

8 + 3 + 3 = 8 + 6 = 14   2 + 8 + 6 = 10 + 6 = 16

2 + 7 + 7 = 2 + 14 = 16   7 + 2 + 8 = 7 + 10 = 17

5 + 6 + 6 = 5 + 12 = 17

PAGE 69

2 + 4 + 6 = 12   3 + 3 + 5 = 11

4 + 4 + 9 = 17   5 + 2 + 8 = 15

3 + 7 + 8 = 18   8 + 8 + 3 = 19

5 + 5 + 9 = 19   3 + 6 + 6 = 15

2 + 9 + 9 = 20   6 + 4 + 7 = 17

PAGE 70

10 pets

8 people

13 animals

15 cards

PAGE 71

2 + 4 + 6 = 12 cans

3 + 7 + 1 = 11 boxes

3 + 3 + 4 = 10 pieces of fruit

PAGE 72

add 7

add 9

add 8

5, 10, 15, 20, 25; add 5

4, 8, 12, 16, 20; add 4

6, 12, 18, 24, 30; add 6

PAGE 73

Rule: add 5		Rule: add 3	
In	Out	In	Out
4	9	5	8
5	10	6	9
6	11	10	13
7	12	11	14
8	13	17	20

PAGE 74

1 ten and 8 ones = 18

2 tens and 9 ones = 29

3 tens and 8 ones = 38

PAGE 75

23 + 2 = 25   31 + 5 = 36

33 + 6 = 39   42 + 4 = 46

50 + 7 = 57   55 + 4 = 59

63 + 5 = 68

PAGE 76

5 tens and 2 ones = 52

7 tens and 4 ones = 74

9 tens and 5 ones = 95

8 tens and 6 ones = 86

PAGE 77

34 + 30 = 64   37 + 50 = 87

52 + 20 = 72   45 + 30 = 75

56 + 30 = 86   64 + 30 = 94

PAGE 78

28 + 10 = 38   17 + 10 = 27

29 + 10 = 39   32 + 10 = 42

54 + 10 = 64   83 + 10 = 93

51 + 20 = 71   42 + 20 = 62

24 + 70 = 94   41 + 40 = 81

37 + 30 = 67   68 + 30 = 98

PAGE 79

3 tens and 7 ones = 37

5 tens and 6 ones = 56

6 tens and 9 ones = 69

8 tens and 7 ones = 87

PAGE 80

34 + 13 = 47   25 + 24 = 49

33 + 33 = 66   31 + 27 = 58

56 + 23 = 79   74 + 11 = 85

PAGE 81

40 + 5 = 45   22 + 6 = 28

36 + 3 = 39   46 + 3 = 49

62 + 2 = 64   83 + 5 = 88

42 + 25 = 67   34 + 14 = 48

25 + 34 = 59   60 + 23 = 83

72 + 25 = 97   63 + 36 = 99

PAGE 82

3 tens and 3 ones = 33

5 tens and 2 ones = 52

PAGE 83

4 tens and 1 one = 41

5 tens and 3 ones = 53

7 tens and 2 ones = 72

PAGE 84

28 + 5 = 33   35 + 7 = 42

44 + 8 = 52   58 + 6 = 64

36 + 9 = 45   47 + 7 = 54

62 + 9 = 71   77 + 6 = 83

PAGE 85

$$
\begin{array}{r} 25 \\ +\ 4 \\ \hline 29 \end{array}
\qquad
\begin{array}{r} 42 \\ +\ 5 \\ \hline 47 \end{array}
\qquad
\begin{array}{r} 31 \\ +\ 5 \\ \hline 36 \end{array}
$$

$$
\begin{array}{r} 54 \\ +\ 4 \\ \hline 58 \end{array}
\qquad
\begin{array}{r} 62 \\ +\ 3 \\ \hline 65 \end{array}
\qquad
\begin{array}{r} 75 \\ +\ 3 \\ \hline 78 \end{array}
$$

PAGE 86

$$
\begin{array}{r} 40 \\ +\ 8 \\ \hline 48 \end{array}
\qquad
\begin{array}{r} 35 \\ +\ 2 \\ \hline 37 \end{array}
\qquad
\begin{array}{r} 22 \\ +\ 6 \\ \hline 28 \end{array}
$$

$$
\begin{array}{r} 42 \\ +\ 4 \\ \hline 46 \end{array}
\qquad
\begin{array}{r} 26 \\ +\ 3 \\ \hline 29 \end{array}
\qquad
\begin{array}{r} 32 \\ +\ 7 \\ \hline 39 \end{array}
$$

$$
\begin{array}{r} 56 \\ +\ 2 \\ \hline 58 \end{array}
\qquad
\begin{array}{r} 71 \\ +\ 8 \\ \hline 79 \end{array}
\qquad
\begin{array}{r} 63 \\ +\ 4 \\ \hline 67 \end{array}
$$

$$
\begin{array}{r} 83 \\ +\ 3 \\ \hline 86 \end{array}
\qquad
\begin{array}{r} 90 \\ +\ 7 \\ \hline 97 \end{array}
\qquad
\begin{array}{r} 94 \\ +\ 5 \\ \hline 99 \end{array}
$$

PAGE 87

$$
\begin{array}{r} 26 \\ +\ 5 \\ \hline 31 \end{array}
\qquad
\begin{array}{r} 43 \\ +\ 9 \\ \hline 52 \end{array}
\qquad
\begin{array}{r} 38 \\ +\ 8 \\ \hline 46 \end{array}
$$

PAGE 88

16	28	23
+ 8	+ 5	+ 8
24	33	31

19	37	46
+ 6	+ 5	+ 4
25	42	50

59	48	74
+ 2	+ 7	+ 8
61	55	82

83	82	65
+ 7	+ 9	+ 8
90	91	73

PAGE 89

46	36	83
+ 2	+ 3	+ 3
48	39	86

48	26	77
+ 5	+ 6	+ 6
53	32	83

52	88	72
+ 8	+ 8	+ 9
60	96	81

PAGE 90

14	45	39
+15	+23	+15
29	68	54

29	43	38
+19	+26	+34
48	69	72

PAGE 91

26	38	22
+14	+15	+36
40	53	58

21	38	42
+39	+38	+23
60	76	65

64	26	27
+13	+55	+45
77	81	72

77	27	56
+12	+53	+38
89	80	94

PAGE 92

$24 + $7 = $31

$14 + $6 = $20

$18 + $6 = $24

PAGE 93

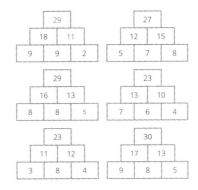

PAGE 94

7 + 3 = 10   2 + 4 = 6

1 + 6 = 7   0 + 3 = 3

4 + 5 = 9   5 + 2 = 7

10 + 0 = 10   3 + 3 = 6

6	8	3
+ 2	+ 1	+ 5
8	9	8

4	3	8
+ 0	+ 2	+ 2
4	5	10

4	2	6
+ 4	+ 7	+ 3
8	9	9

PAGE 95

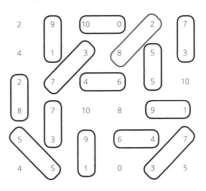

PAGE 96

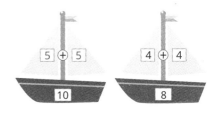

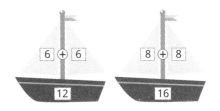

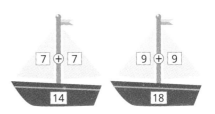

PAGE 97

9 + 4 = 13   8 + 3 = 11

6 + 6 = 12   7 + 5 = 12

5 + 9 = 14   6 + 8 = 14

9 + 2 = 11   8 + 8 = 16

6	5	9
+ 7	+ 8	+ 9
13	13	18

5	4	8
+ 6	+ 9	+ 9
11	13	17

8	9	7
+ 4	+ 7	+ 8
12	16	15

PAGE 98

Order of numbers in answers may vary.

3 + 7 = 10   4 + 7 = 11

2 + 9 = 11   8 + 5 = 13

1 + 9 = 10   5 + 7 = 12

6 + 8 = 14   4 + 9 = 13

6 + 7 = 13   4 + 7 = 11

8 + 9 = 17   3 + 9 = 12

PAGE 99

Arrangement of pairs of numbers may vary. Some possible arrangements are shown below.

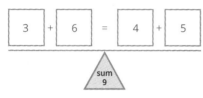

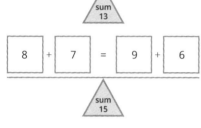

PAGE 100

4 + 6 + 3 = 13	5 + 5 + 8 = 18
5 + 6 + 9 = 20	7 + 3 + 4 = 14
6 + 6 + 3 = 15	5 + 7 + 8 = 20

Answers may vary. Some possible answers are shown below.

3 + 2 + 5 = 10

2 + 3 + 7 = 12

1 + 5 + 9 = 15

8 + 7 + 5 = 20

PAGE 101

$7

cakes

14 animals

Brenda

PAGE 102

15	28	22
+ 4	+ 3	+ 7
19	31	29

PAGE 102, *continued*

19	31	44
+ 9	+ 6	+ 8
28	37	52

45	56	72
+ 3	+ 2	+ 9
48	58	81

85	69	76
+ 5	+ 4	+ 5
90	73	81

PAGE 103

35	21	24
+13	+15	+13
48	36	37

36	42	49
+ 6	+ 6	+10
42	48	59

33	24	39
+14	+ 4	+ 9
47	28	48

43	34	52
+ 8	+32	+17
51	66	69

71	62	29
+12	+ 6	+12
83	68	41

61	58	32
+ 4	+ 7	+33
65	65	65

PAGE 104

57 cents

50 cents

PAGE 105

79 cents

No. Jeff needs only 77 cents.

Yes. Amy needs 99 cents.